THE CHILD JESUS

BY FLORENCE MARY FITCH

ILLUSTRATED BY LEONARD WEISGARD

LOTHROP, LEE AND SHEPARD COMPANY, INC · NEW YORK

Library of Congress Catalog Card Number: 55-10438

THE CHILD JESUS

Would you like me to tell you about Jesus when he was a little boy? That was long ago in a country far away, so we cannot know exactly how he lived and what he did. But we can picture some of the things that may have happened when Jesus was living in Nazareth with his parents, Mary and Joseph.

Nazareth was a busy little city with low stone houses crowded close together. Many of them had little shops in front, all open to the street in the daytime and closed with heavy shutters at night. Joseph had a carpenter shop.

Narrow paths climbed up the hills that surrounded Nazareth and on the slopes were the gardens and orchards and vineyards of the families who lived down in the city.

The little house where Jesus lived was full of life. Each morning before the sun rose, the rooster began to crow. Sometimes it wakened Jesus and then he watched his father as he stood near the window to worship God, and heard him repeat, "Thou shalt love the Lord thy God with all thy heart and with all thy soul and with all thy might." Jesus heard the words so often that he knew them by heart.

These same words were written on a scroll which was kept in a small box fastened to the door-frame. Jesus was taught to touch the box whenever he went into or came out of the house and then to kiss his hand. This was to show God that He was remembered.

Jesus liked to say the beautiful words and he made up a little tune and sang over and over: "Love the Lord, love the Lord with all thy heart!"

Sometimes in the evening Joseph would go to the chest where all the dearest family treasures were kept and take out a parchment scroll, part of the holy book. Then Jesus would stand close to him as he unrolled it on his knee and began to read. When he came to "Love the Lord," Jesus always looked at the words and recited them with Joseph.

One day Jesus picked up a sharp stone and tried to scratch the letters of the three words on a piece of a broken jar. Another day, in Joseph's shop, he scratched them on a bit of wood. Joseph was very proud that his little boy had taught himself to read and write the three important words. He fastened the board against the wall as a motto for his shop.

Jesus liked to work with Joseph. He could hand his father whatever tool he wanted and put away the one not in use. He could hold a board while Joseph sawed it in two and smoothed it with his sharp knife until it was as smooth as velvet. He learned to drive a nail straight without hammering his finger. He could whittle with his own special knife.

One afternoon Joseph said proudly, "This bowl is finished, smooth enough for anyone's kneading."

"Oh, can we take it to David's mother?" Jesus begged. "She has no bread bowl."

"Well then, we'll surprise her with this one," said Joseph. And when the day's work was done and the shop shutters were tightly closed, Joseph and Jesus went to David's home.

FIRST UNITED PRESBYTERIAN CHURCH
NORWALK, OHIO

While Joseph went in to see David's mother, the boys played in the dooryard with stones smooth and round as marbles. When they tired of that, they watched the lazy lizard sunning himself, then scurrying away when startled.

As Joseph and Jesus walked toward their own home in the gathering dusk, Jesus looked up and said, "David thinks you are the kindest man in Nazareth."

Joseph did not reply but he smiled and laid his hand tenderly on the little boy's head.

Jesus liked to be with his mother, too. It was fun to take turns at the handle of the little mill that ground the wheat into flour, to watch the bread dough rising higher and higher in the bowl, and to see Mary shape the little loaves and put them in the clay oven. He liked to shake the black bag of skin in which the goats' milk was churned into butter. And he loved the crackling fire over which a big kettle of beans boiled for the evening meal.

When Mary sat on the doorstep, spinning or sewing, they talked of many things that a little boy wants to know.

Jesus often went with Mary to the spring where fresh water came sparkling out of the rock, clear and cool. This was the only fresh water in the entire town, so all the women went there every day to fill their large water jars. Jesus was sure to find other children there, wading in the pool or floating bits of wood. Sometimes he would blow a happy tune on his little reed pipe and the boys and girls would follow him, dancing and singing as they had seen their elders do in wedding processions.

In the spring, as soon as the rains were over and gone, everyone went up on the hills. The women planted gardens and the men plowed fields and pruned orchards. All around them doves cooed to their mates and white-throated robins sang of love. Golden sunshine flooded the earth. New green leaves appeared on the bare branches of the fig trees, silvery leaves on the olive trees, and rosy-tipped gray leaves on the grape vines. Fresh grass sprang up among the bare rocks and everywhere flowers bloomed—pink flax, yellow daisies, red poppies, blue forget-me-nots, and many others—the wonderful carpet God had spread for the festival of spring.

Jesus often clambered up the hills alone. He liked to look for the honey the wild bees hid in hollows in the rocks. And sometimes a field sparrow would fly up from its nest on the ground and then he would see the four spotted eggs—so like the stones that only very keen eyes would notice them. Once a fox stuck his head out of a hole and stared in silence when he saw Jesus.

And always, in the springtime, a little tinkling stream made music as it hurried down the shallow valley. Jesus leaped from rock to rock and danced about, singing his own little song, "Love the Lord, love the Lord with all thy heart."

One day Joseph said that the foxes were nibbling his grape vines and he would have to set a trap or they would have no grapes in the fall.

"But foxes are hungry, too," Jesus said, remembering the bright eyes he had seen on the hill. "And where would the little foxes get their food?"

Joseph explained that foxes must learn to find food for themselves without stealing what men have planted for their children. Jesus understood, but still he felt sorry for the foxes, for they had children, too.

So the grapes grew on the vines into large juicy clusters and the time of the harvest came. All the relatives came to the festival and Joseph and Mary brought a family who had just settled in Nazareth and who had no vineyard of their own.

Everyone, even the children, helped with the picking. But Jesus was careful not to take all the grapes from the vines. He left a few clusters for the fox to take home to its children. Then he helped fill broad baskets for the women to carry on their heads, and large deep ones to hang on each side of the donkeys' backs, and still others for the men to swing over their shoulders. When the harvest was gathered they stopped to rest and ate their lunch—bread and cheese and olives and all the grapes they could eat. Then Joseph said thank you to God for giving them the good earth, the sunshine, the rain, the strength to work, and the rich harvest.

And they all sang
together the harvest song,
"Praise the Lord for He is good,"

as they carried
their precious loads
down the hill.

It was beginning to grow dark when Joseph, Mary and Jesus reached home. The sheep and the goats came down from the hillside where they had been all day. The ox and the donkey found the manger where they fed. The chickens went to roost, the swallow spread her protecting wings over her nest, and the little ants were all sheltered under the big stone which covered their home. Then Joseph shut the door and lighted the lamp. Even if the wind should blow and rain come, all would be safe and snug within. And again Joseph thanked God...for the happy day, for His protecting care, and for His gift of sleep.

Mary spread upon the floor the mats which were their beds, and Jesus fell asleep, singing to himself *Love the Lord with all thy heart*. And the little lamp burned all through the night, reaching every corner with its soft light.